Elgar Piano Album

arranged by Desmond Ratcliffe

NOVELLO

Contents

THEME
from 'Enigma Variations'
Opus 36

NIMROD
from 'Enigma Variations'
Opus 36

CHANSON DE MATIN

Opus 15, No. 2

6

Tempo I

poco cresc.

poco rit.

pp dolciss.

accel.

a tempo

più tranquillo

cresc.

dolce

20178

OPENING THEME
from Symphony No. 1
Opus 55

Andante, nobilmente e semplice ♩ = 72

SERENADE
from 'The Wand of Youth' Suite 1
Opus 1a

CHANSON DE NUIT

Opus 15. No. 1

poco stringendo

Tempo I

ANGEL'S FAREWELL
from 'The Dream of Gerontius'
Opus 38

ADAGIO
from the Cello Concerto
Opus 85

CANTO POPOLARE
from the Concert Overture 'In the South'
Opus 50

IMPERIAL MARCH

Opus 32

largamente

animato

allargando

9/95 (22464)

MUSIC FOR PIANO SOLO

ORIGINAL COMPOSITIONS

Allegro – Concert Solo
Music for Piano *an album of five pieces:*

> *My Song*
> *Carrisima*
> *Echo's Dream*
> *Rosemary*
> *Beau Brummel*

Presto and Griffinesque
Two piano pieces:

> In Smyrna
> Skizze

ARRANGEMENTS

Chanson de Matin *arranged by Thomson*
Chanson de Nuit *arranged by Thomson*
Enigma Variations, The *arranged by the composer*
Nimrod, *from The Enigma Variations, arranged by the composer*
Starlight Express, The *a suite for piano selected from the incidental music for the play. Arranged by Kettèlbey*
Elgar Piano Album *ten arrangements by Desmond Ratcliffe:*

Theme from Enigma Variations	Serenade from 'Wand of Youth' Suite 1
Nimrod	Angel's Farewell from 'The Dream of Gerontius'
Chanson de Matin	Canto Popolare from 'In the South'
Chanson de Nuit	Imperial March
Opening Theme from Symphony No 1	Adagio from the Cello Concerto

NOVELLO PUBLISHING

8/9 Frith Street, London W1V 5TZ.

Exclusive distributors:
Music Sales Limited
Newmarket Road, Bury St. Edmunds,
Suffolk IP33 3YB.

ISBN 0-85360-605-6

9 780853 606055

Order No. NOV 100220

HARWICH •

A 100 Years of Service
100 Jaar Veerdienst

HOEK VAN HOLLAND

HARWICH • HOOK OF HOLLAND
100 YEARS
1893 1993

MILES COWSILL   FRANK HAALMEIJER   JOHN HENDY

StenaLine
WORLD'S LEADING FERRY COMPANY

GOEDKOOPE
RETOURS NAAR:
ENGELAND & SCHOTLAND
via VLISSINGEN & HOEK v. HOLLAND
HARWICH